Robbie Williams Easy Keyboard

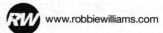 www.robbiewilliams.com

Published 2002
Editor Chris Harvey
Cover Photograhy Louis Sanchis

Music arranged and processed
by Barnes Music Engraving Ltd
East Sussex TN34 1HA

© International Music
Publications Limited

ANGELS

Words and Music by Robert Williams and Guy Chambers

Suggested Registration: Electric Piano / Solo Flute
Rhythm: 16 Beat
Tempo: ♩ = 76

I sit and wait,_____ does an an - gel con-tem-plate__ my fate?

And do they know__ the pla-ces where we go___ when we're grey and old?__

'Cos I have been told___ that sal-va - tion lets their wings__ un - fold.__

__ So when I'm ly-ing in my bed,___ thoughts run-ning through my head_____ and I

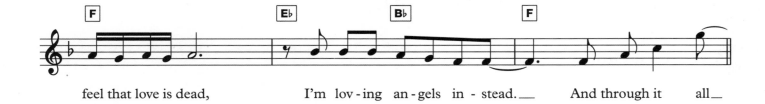

feel that love is dead, I'm lov-ing an-gels in - stead.__ And through it all__

__ she of-fers me pro-tec - tion, a lot of love and af-fec - tion, whe-ther I'm right or

wrong. And down the wa - ter-fall___ wher-ev-er it__ may take__ me, I know that life won't break

__ me, when I come to call.___ She won't for - sake___ me,

I'm lov - ing an - gels in - stead.__ When I'm feel-ing weak_ and my pain

__ walks down a one-way street, I look a-bove__ and I know

__ I'll al - ways be blessed with love. And as the feel-ing grows, she brings

flesh to my bones_ and when love is dead, I'm lov-ing an-gels in-stead._ And through it all

ETERNITY

Words and Music by Robert Williams and Guy Chambers

Suggested Registration: Vibraphone / Strings
Rhythm: 8 Beat
Tempo: ♩ = 79

Close your eyes so you don't feel them, they don't need to see you

cry. I can't pro-mise I will heal you,

but if you want___ to I will try.

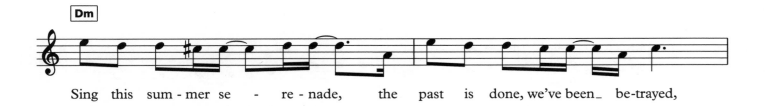

Sing this sum-mer se - re - nade, the past is done, we've been___ be-trayed,

it's true.___ Some-one said the truth will out___ and

HAVE YOU MET MISS JONES?

Words by Lorenz Hart / Music by Richard Rodgers

Suggested Registration: Brass
Rhythm: Swing
Tempo: ♩ = 124

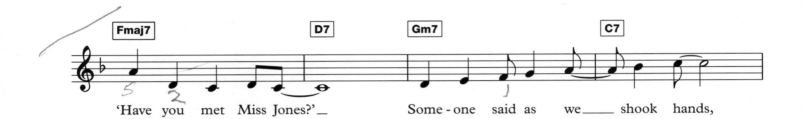

'Have you met Miss Jones?'— Some-one said as we__ shook hands,

she was just__ Miss Jones__ to me._____ And

then I said 'Miss Jones,__ you're a girl who un-der-stands,

I'm a man who must__ be free.'_____ And all at

once I lost my breath,__ and all at once was scared to death,

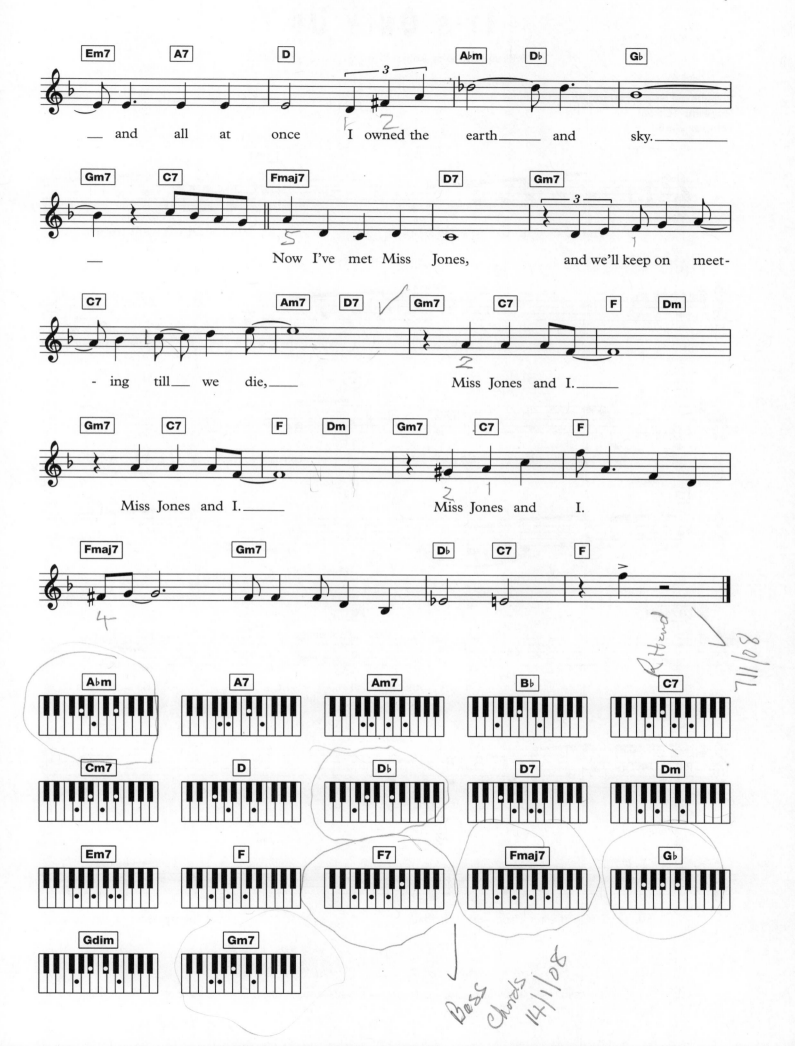

It's Only Us

Words and Music by Robert Williams and Guy Chambers

Suggested Registration: Acoustic Guitar
Rhythm: 16 Beat
Tempo: ♩ = 88

KIDS

Words and Music by Robert Williams and Guy Chambers

Suggested Registration: Electric Guitar / Synth Strings
Rhythm: 16 Beat Funk
Tempo: ♩ = 93

Let Love Be Your Energy

Words and Music by Robert Williams and Guy Chambers

Suggested Registration: Saxophone / Strings
Rhythm: 8 Beat Funk
Tempo: ♩ = 88

Out of a mil - li - on seeds,_____ on - ly the

strong - est one breathes._____ You made a mi -

- ra - cle mo - ther, I'll make a man out of me.____

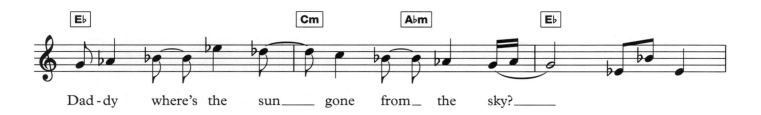

Dad - dy where's the sun____ gone from_ the sky?_____

What did we__ do wrong?__ Why did__ it die?

Let Me Entertain You

Words and Music by Robert Williams and Guy Chambers

Suggested Registration: Brass / Strings
Rhythm: 8 Beat / Disco
Tempo: ♩ = 124

Hell is gone and hea-ven's here, there's no-thing left__ for you to fear,

shake your arse come ov-er here, now scream. I'm a burn-ing ef-fi-gy__ of

ev-ery-thing I used to be, you're my rock of em-pa-thy, my

dear. So come on let me__ en-ter-tain__ you.__

Let me__ en-ter-tain__ you.

Life's too short for you to die,__ so grab your-self__ an a-li-bi,

Mack The Knife

Words by Bertholt Brecht / Music by Kurt Weill / Translation by Marc Blitzstein

Suggested Registration: Trumpet / Strings
Rhythm: Swing
Tempo: ♩ = 160

Oh the shark babe, ___ has such

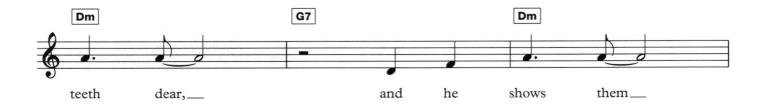

teeth dear, ___ and he shows them ___

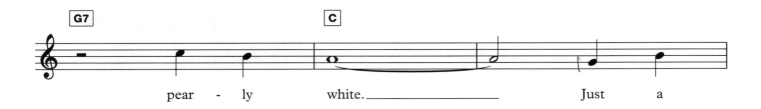

pear - ly white. ___ Just a

jack - knife ___ has old Mac - heath babe, ___

___ and he keeps it ___ out of

sight. ___ Yeah, yeah, ___ Jen - ny

Millennium

Words and Music by Robert Williams, Guy Chambers, John Barry and Leslie Bricusse

Suggested Registration: Piano / Strings
Rhythm: 16 Beat
Tempo: ♩ = 84

Some say that we are play-ers, some say that we_ are pawns, but we've been mak-ing mon-ey since the day that we were born, got to slow down,___ 'cos we're low_ down.

Run a-round in cir-cles, live a life of so-li-tude, till we find our-selves a part-ner, some-one to re-late_ to,___ then we'll slow down,___ be-fore we_ fall_ down.

We've got stars___ di-rect-ing our fate,

and we're pray - ing it's_ not too late,_ 'cos we know we're fall - ing from grace.

_ Mil - len - ni - um._____

Come and have_ a go____ if you_ think you_ are high_ e - nough. _

Come and have_ a go____ if you_ think you_ are hard_ e - nough.

_ Mil - len - ni - um._____ Mil - len - ni - um.

We've got stars____ di - rect - ing our fate,

_ and we're pray - ing it's_ not too late,____ 'cos we know

repeat to fade

_ we're fall - ing from grace._ Mil-len-ni - um,_____ We've got stars

No Regrets

Words and Music by Robert Williams and Guy Chambers

Suggested Registration: 12 String Guitar / Strings
Rhythm: 8 Beat
Tempo: ♩ = 104

No re - grets,___ they don't work.___

No re - grets,___ now,_ they on - ly hurt.___

Sing me a love___ song, drop me a line._

Sup-pose it's just___ a point_ of view,

but they tell___ me I'm do - ing fine.___

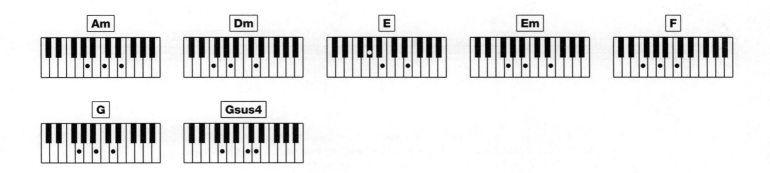

Old Before I Die

Words and Music by Robert Williams, Eric Bazilian and Desmond Child

Suggested Registration: 12 String Guitar / Electric Piano
Rhythm: 8 Beat
Tempo: ♩ = 116

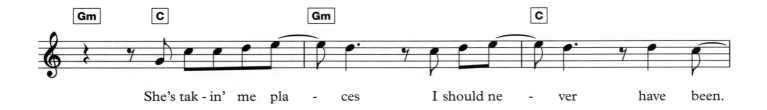

She's tak-in' me pla - ces I should ne - ver have been.

_ She's show-in' me fa - ces I should ne -

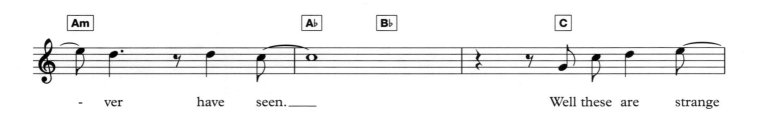

- ver have seen.___ Well these are strange

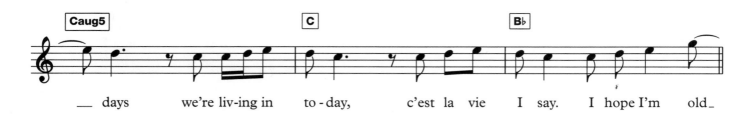

_ days we're liv-ing in to - day, c'est la vie I say. I hope I'm old_

_ be - fore I die,_____

One For My Baby

Words by Johnny Mercer / Music by Harold Arlen

Suggested Registration: Piano / Jazz Guitar
Rhythm: Swing
Tempo: ♩ = 90

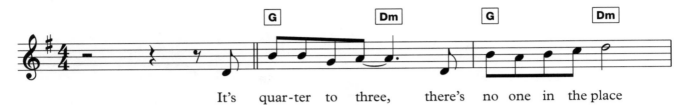

It's quar-ter to three, there's no one in the place

'cept you and me. So set 'em up Joe, ___ I

got a lit-tle sto-ry I think you should know. We're

drink-ing my friend, to the end of a brief ___ e-pi-sode. Make it

one for my ba-by, and one more for the road.

You'd ne-ver know it, but bud-dy I'm a kind of po-et, and I've

Phoenix From The Flames

Words and Music by Robert Williams and Guy Chambers

Suggested Registration: Studio Piano
Rhythm: Pop Ballad
Tempo: ♩ = 76

Si - lence shields the rain,__ so you say no-thing. Feel they've rigged the game,

__ and you've done with lov-in'. On - ly you__ can see__ the dark-

- ness in the north-ern lights. Phoe - nix from the flames, we will rise__ to-geth-er.

They will know our names, can you feel__ it? Shel - ter me__ from pain,

__ I al-ways wan-na feel this way,_____ oh yeah.__

Ev-'ry-bo-dy's talk-ing, no - bo-dy's list'n-ing, too bu-sy think-in' 'bout what you've been miss-ing.

Ev-'ry-bo-dy said you're gon - na take__ it too__ far ba - by

The Road To Mandalay

Words and Music by Robert Williams and Guy Chambers

Suggested Registration: Solo Flute / Strings
Rhythm: 8 Beat
Tempo: ♩ = 98

Rock DJ

Words and Music by Robert Williams, Guy Chambers, Kelvin Andrews, Nelson Pigford and Ekundayo Paris

Suggested Registration: Saxophone / Brass
Rhythm: 8 Beat Funky Pop
Tempo: ♩ = 104

31

She's The One

Words and Music by Karl Wallinger

Suggested Registration: Piano / Strings
Rhythm: 8 Beat
Tempo: ♩ = 78

I was her, _____ she was me, _____ we were one, _

_ we were free. _____ And if there's some-bo - dy call-ing me on, _

_____ she's the one. ___ If there's some-bo - dy call-ing me on,

_____ she's the one. ___ We were young,

_ we were wrong, ___ we were free ___ all a - long. ___ If there's some-bo -

- dy call-ing me on, _____ she's the one. ___

When you get to where you wan-na go, ___ and you know the things you wan-na know, you're

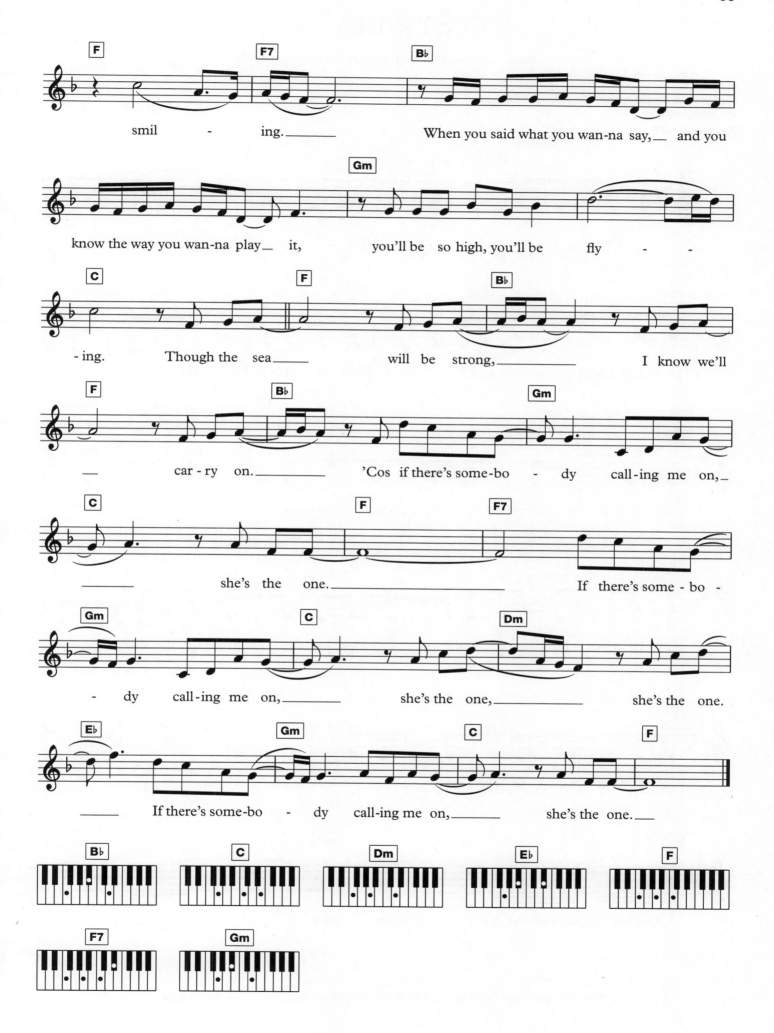

STRONG

Words and Music by Robert Williams and Guy Chambers

Suggested Registration: Pop Organ / Strings
Rhythm: 16 Beat
Tempo: ♩ = 86

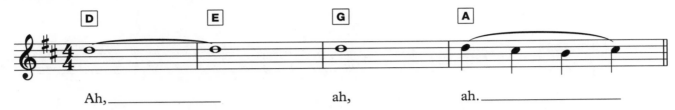

Ah,_____ ah, ah._____

My breath smells of a thou-sand fags_ and when I'm drunk I dance like me Dad, I've

start - ed to dress_ a bit_ like him._____ And

ear - ly morn - ing when I wake up, I look like Kiss but with-out the make-up and

that's a good line to take it to the bridge._____

And you know, and you know 'cause my life's a_____ mess,_____

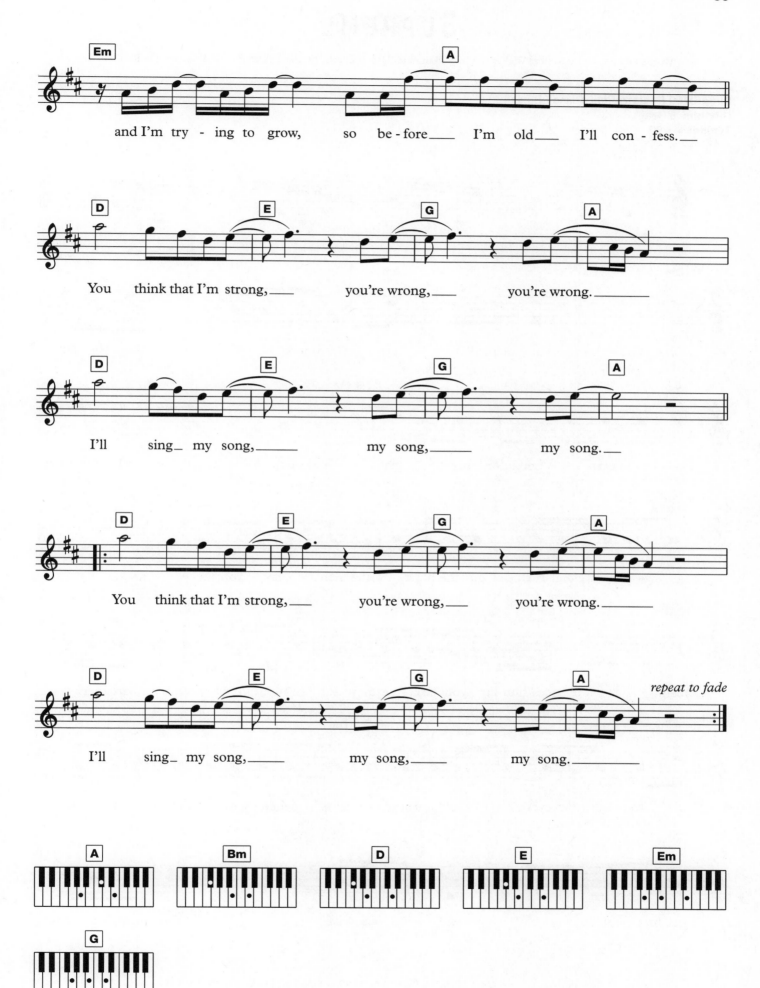

Supreme

Words and Music by Robert Williams, Guy Chambers, Dino Fekaris, Frederick Perren and Francois De Roubaix

Suggested Registration: Piano / Brass
Rhythm: 8 Beat
Tempo: ♩ = 96

Oh, it seemed for - ev - er stopped to - day,___ all the lone -

- ly hearts in Lon - don caught a plane___ and flew a - way.___ And all the best

___ wo - men are mar - ried, all the hand - some men are gay, you feel de - prived.

Yeah, are you ques - tion-ing your size, is there a tu - mour in your hu - mour, are there bags

___ un - der your eyes?___ Do you leave dents where you sit, are you

get - ting on___ a bit, will you sur - vive?___ You must sur - vive.

THEY CAN'T TAKE THAT AWAY FROM ME

Music and Lyrics by George Gershwin and Ira Gershwin

Suggested Registration: Vibraphone / Jazz Guitar
Rhythm: Swing
Tempo: ♩ = 120

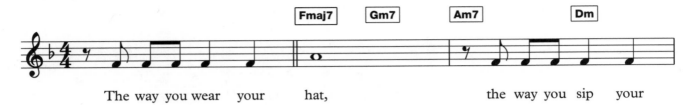

The way you wear your hat, the way you sip your

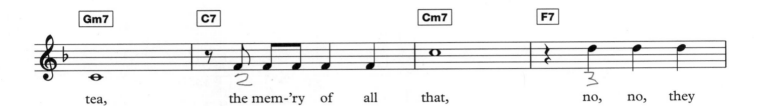

tea, the mem-'ry of all that, no, no, they

can't take that a - way from me. The way your smile just beams,

the way you sing off key. The way you haunt my dreams,

oh no, they can't take that a - way from me. We may

ne - ver, ne - ver meet a - gain on this bum - py road to

THINGS

Words and Music by Bobby Darin

Suggested Registration: Brass
Rhythm: Swing
Tempo: ♩ = 170

Ev - ery night I sit here by my

win - dow,___ (win - dow),___ star - ing at the

lone - ly a - ve - nue, (a - ve - nue), watch - ing lo - vers

hold - ing hands and laugh - ing,___ (ha, ha, ha,)

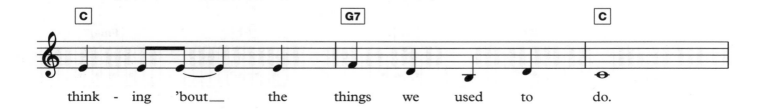

think - ing 'bout___ the things we used to do.

Piano/Vocal/Guitar
Order Reference: 9237A
ISBN: 1-84328-035-3

I WILL TALK AND HOLLYWOOD WILL LISTEN

MACK THE KNIFE

SOMETHIN' STUPID

DO NOTHIN' TILL YOU HEAR FROM ME

IT WAS A VERY GOOD YEAR

STRAIGHTEN UP AND FLY RIGHT

WELL, DID YOU EVAH

MR. BOJANGLES

ONE FOR MY BABY

THINGS

AIN'T THAT A KICK IN THE HEAD

THEY CAN'T TAKE THAT AWAY FROM ME

HAVE YOU MET MISS JONES?

ME AND MY SHADOW
(AS PERFORMED BY SAMMY DAVIS, JR. AND FRANK SINATRA)

BEYOND THE SEA

Available from all good music shops

 www.robbiewilliams.com

RW1

LIFE THRU A LENS

Piano/Vocal/Guitar
Order Reference: 5853A
ISBN: 1-85909-540-2

LAZY DAYS
LIFE THRU A LENS
EGO A GO GO
ANGELS
SOUTH OF THE BORDER
OLD BEFORE I DIE
ONE OF GOD'S BETTER PEOPLE
LET ME ENTERTAIN YOU
KILLING ME
CLEAN
BABY GIRL WINDOW

I'VE BEEN EXPECTING YOU

Piano/Vocal/Guitar
Order Reference: 6645A
ISBN: 1-85909-628-X

STRONG
NO REGRETS
MILLENNIUM
PHOENIX FROM THE FLAMES
WIN SOME LOSE SOME
GRACE
JESUS IN A CAMPER VAN
HEAVEN FROM HERE
KARMA KILLER
SHE'S THE ONE
MAN MACHINE
THESE DREAMS
STAND YOUR GROUND
STALKERS DAY OFF

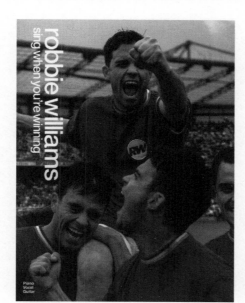

SING WHEN YOU'RE WINNING

Piano/Vocal/Guitar
Order Reference: 7591A
ISBN: 1-85909-927-0

LET LOVE BE YOUR ENERGY
BETTER MAN
ROCK DJ
SUPREME
KIDS
IF IT'S HURTING YOU
SINGING FOR THE LONELY
LOVE CALLING EARTH
KNUTSFORD CITY LIMITS
FOREVER TEXAS
BY ALL MEANS NECESSARY
THE ROAD TO MANDALAY

Available from all good music shops

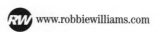 www.robbiewilliams.com

www.robbiewilliams.com